A MESSAGE TO PARENTS

Reading good books to young children is a crucial factor in a child's psychological and intellectual development. It promotes a mutually warm and satisfying relationship between parent and child and enhances the child's awareness of the world around him. It stimulates the child's imagination and lays a foundation for the development of the skills necessary to support the critical thinking process. In addition, the parent who reads to his child helps him to build vocabulary and other prerequisite skills for the child's own successful reading.

In order to provide parents and children with books which will do these things, Brown Watson has published this series of small books specially designed for young children. These books are factual, fanciful, humorous, questioning and adventurous. A library acquired in this inexpensive way will provide many hours of pleasurable and profitable reading for parents and children.

Published by Brown Watson (Leicester) Ltd.
ENGLAND
© 1980 Rand McNally & Company
Printed and bound in the German Democratic Republic.

Baby
Animals

By NAOMA ZIMMERMAN

Illustrated by
MARGE OPITZ

Brown Watson

England.

Floppy puppy
    likes to chew,
So let him have
    a worn-out shoe.

Hear this little
donkey bray
"He-haw, he-haw,
here I stay."

Little goose has
a stiff-legged walk
And says
"Honk, honk" when
he tries to talk.

Gentle calf in
  the clover lies,
Munching grass
  and shooing flies.

Ducky waddles
down the path
And quacks,
"I'm going
to take a bath."

Little field mouse,
soft and grey,
Squeaks and
scampers through
the hay.

Baby pig is pink
 and sweet,
He squeals a lot
 and likes to eat.

Woolly lamb,
when his
playmates call,
Bounces off like
a popcorn ball.

Jumping colt
  will run all day,
Stopping just
  to nibble hay.

Baby squirrel is
in a hurry,
With cheeks so full
and tail
so furry.

Baby billy goat
likes to butt,
His head is
as hard
as a coconut.

When bunny moves,
he always hops –
His nose has
a wiggle
that never stops.

Of all the animals
on the farm,
Kitty feels
nicest
in my arm.